Mike Barton lives in Solana Beach, Ca and is the photographer and author of ten photography books including *San Diego's North Coast.*

Shon Watkins is an illustrator from Idaho. Mike designed the scenes using photographs and Shon created original illustrations from these scenes.

Enjoy my book,
Magic ♡

MAGIC

Published by Boulder Press, Solana Beach, Ca, © 2015 Boulder Press
Magics website: www.adventuresofmagic.com.   cell phone 720 934-4322.

1. Stories in rhyme. 2. San Diego (Ca) - Description and travel. 3. Children - travel - San Diego (Ca).

Library of Congress Control Number: 2015944910
ISBN 13:978-0-9899268-3-6
First Printing: 2015 - Printed in China

Magic
visits
San Diego's North Coast

written by Mike Barton

illustrated by Shon Watkins and Mike Barton

As Magic soared above the sea,
she spotted the shore and shouted with glee!

"There's La Jolla, Del Mar and Solana Beach.
Cardiff, Encinitas are well within reach.

Let's go to La Jolla, there's a lovable cove,
where slippery seals waddle and rove.

How do seals surf without a board?
They float on all the **blubber** they've stored.

They play all day on big Seal Rock.
Their barking sound is **just seal talk**.

"Watch how we waddle," said her seal pup friend.
"Just lay on your belly and **scoot your back end**."

Birch Aquarium's like an underwater zoo,
where fabulous fish swim out of the blue.

Seahorses, blowfish, a turtle with fins,
the jellyfish look like identical twins!

There's something lurking in the dark.
"YIKES!" said Magic, "It's a SHARK!"

As Magic sailed in her glider kite,
Torrey Pines came into sight.

While soaring high above the shore, she said,
"When I play golf I don't keep score."

There's a goofer golfer in a green golf cart.
The elephant grunted, "That's **not too SMART!**"

There's a peaceful place called Torrey Pines Reserve.
It's a special space that we need to preserve.

Torrey Pines has trails to the sea.
It's also the name of a very rare tree.

Hikers

Hackers

Rocky

As red-tailed hawks and ravens fly around,
long-tailed weasels and rabbits rule the ground.

Magic hiked up hills and raced down ravines,
and somehow sneaked a snack in between.

Let's go to the fair on the 4th of July,
where fireworks flash and light up the sky.

When Magic's on the slippery slide,
all the kids steer AWAY to the side.

With bumper boats and a monkey maze,
Magic can play for days and days.

There's cotton candy and bacon-wrapped fries,
It's junk food city and all **SUPER SIZED!**

There's a place in Del Mar where dogs run free.

Dog Beach is a blast - your pooch will agree.

Dogs see the beach and start to smile,
they want to stay and play for awhile.

Tennis balls bounce and frisbees fly,
and **happy dogs go dashing by.**

As her furry friends played tag in the tide,
Magic went for a **wild wave ride.**

The track in Del Mar is where people go,
to pick a horse - **win, place or show**.

Seabiscuit is a famous horse.
He made his fame on this old course.

Jockeys all wear colorful shirts.
The horses race on turf and dirt.

DEL MAR
Where the SURF meets the TURF

It's a photo finish but everyone knows,
that **Magic always wins by a nose.**

Solana Beach is the "Gateway to Sunshine,"
and Magic knows it's **gonna be a fun time**.

The trail twists along the tracks.
Pick up the slack and join the pack.

Cardiff
Carlsbad
Del Mar
Encinitas
Oceanside
Beach

MAGIC

There's a thundering sound when trains burst by.

If trains had wings they'd try to fly.

There's a cool campground in Cardiff-by-the-Sea,
with campers and tents as far as you can see.

The Cardiff Kook strikes a surfer pose.
People dress him up in **cuckoo clothes**.

The COASTER train is super fast.
When Magic's driving **it's a blast**.

Now hop aboard and take a ride,
between San Diego and Oceanside.

RAILROAD CROSSING

2105   2105

COASTER

Down to Swami's Beach below the big bluffs,
you can swim or surf and other fun stuff.

Surfers swarm when the waves are high,
and the rocky reefs hide in the tide.

The kids are hip and the **surfers** are a hoot.
Bring a boogie board and your swimming suit.

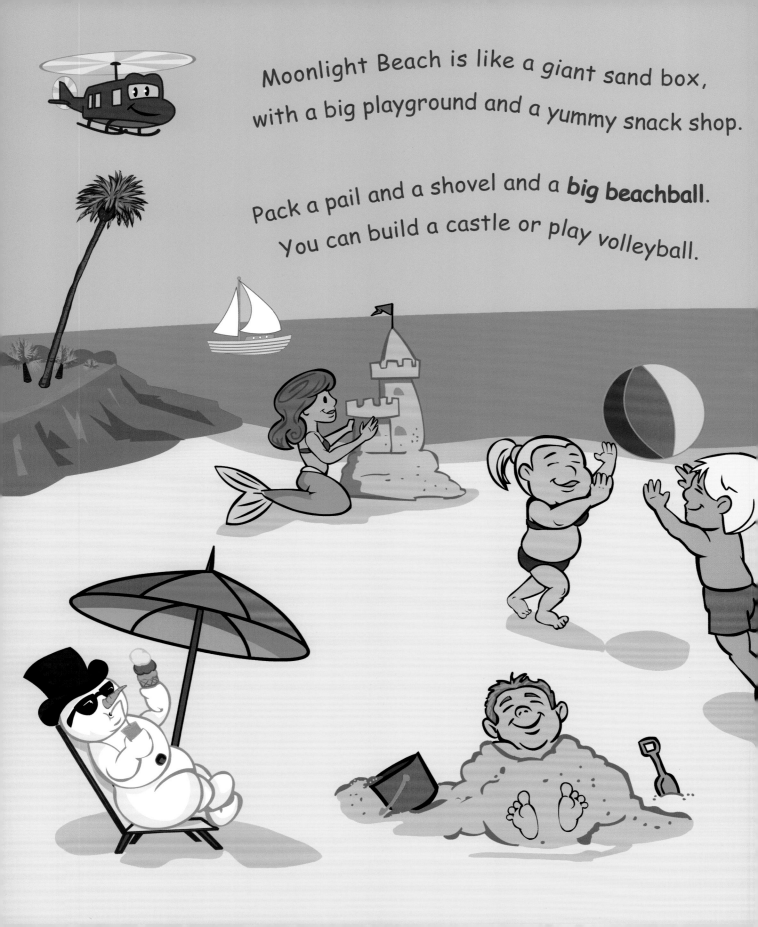

Moonlight Beach is like a giant sand box,
with a big playground and a yummy snack shop.

Pack a pail and a shovel and a **big beachball**.
You can build a castle or play volleyball.

Above the beach, way **HIGH** in the sky, there are **jets and helicopters flying by.**

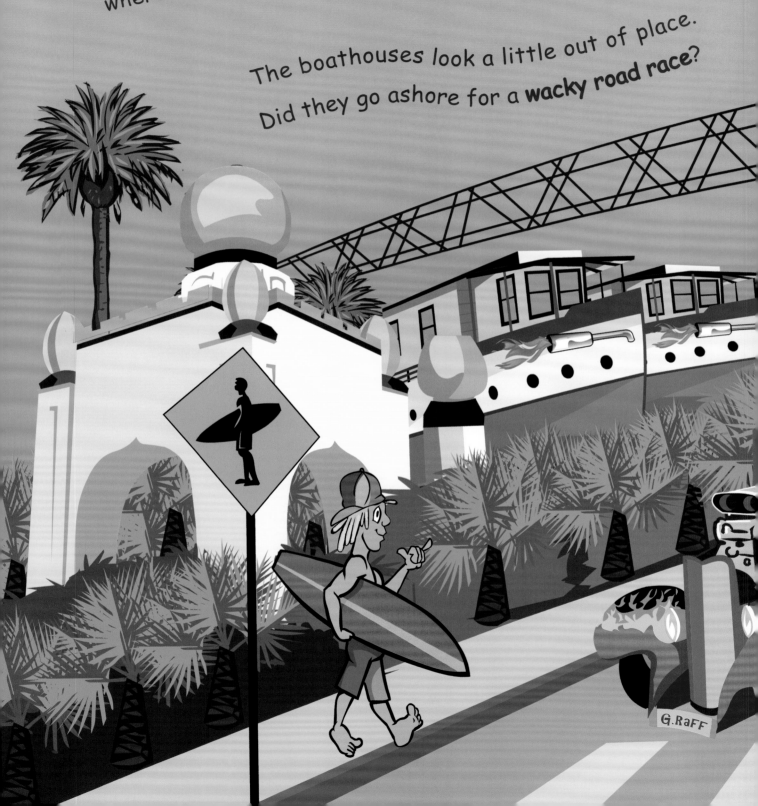

On to Encinitas with the golden domes,
where a peaceful swami had his home.

The boathouses look a little out of place.
Did they go ashore for a **wacky road race**?

Along the beach this groovy surf town,
has hot rods and woody cars cruising around.

The Botanical Gardens have flowers and plants,
where **bunches of butterflies gather to dance.**

In the Elephant Foot Forest is Toni's Tree House.
You can climb up rope ladders like a large jungle mouse.

Let's go to LEGOLAND, a theme park made of bricks,
with water parks and rides and a castle just for kicks.

They have many friendly dinosaurs.
Ye must explore the Pirate Shores.

When the flowers bloom in Carlsbad,
the hummingbirds and bees are glad.

Take a wagon ride among the flowers,
where **Magic runs and jumps for hours.**

The flowers bloom from March to May,
and the old Dutch windmill spins all day.

As the sun began to set there was a **great green FLASH**, and the leaping dolphins danced with a **splish - splash - splash.**

As her hot-air balloon began a gentle climb, Magic said, "**I had a rootin'-tootin' time.**"